Beware
Madame
La Guillotine

Travel to the French Revolution
with Murderess Charlotte Corday

SARAH TOWLE

Beware Madame la Guillotine
Copyright © 2014 by Sarah Towle

Time Traveler Tales
is a division of
Time Traveler Tours, LLC
12 Timber Creek Lane
Newark, DE 19711

ISBN: 978-0-9887418-2-9

Cover Design: Beth Lower

www.timetravelertours.com

To Jim, my better half, for risking all with me.

Contents

Part One
CRISIS

CHAPTER ONE

Meet Charlotte

My name is Marie-Anne Charlotte de Corday d'Armont, but you may call me Charlotte.

Three days ago, I killed a man. I stabbed him through the heart as he soaked in the bath. I am now in prison and facing death, but I do not regret my act. I did it for my country; I did it for France. I did it to avenge my king, Louis XVI (16th), whose beheading was called for by the very man I murdered: the journalist Jean-Paul Marat. I did it to preserve the true goals of the French Revolution, which has recently turned from a movement of hope to a *reign of terror.*

Charlotte Corday

I am 24 years old. In 15 days I will be 25, though I will not live to celebrate my birthday. People admire me for my curly chestnut hair, my dimpled chin, and twinkling grey eyes. What they don't realize is that I'm also well educated.

You see, I was born into an old noble family from Normandy, a province in the northwest of France just across the ocean channel from England. Though my father is not rich, he descends from the great French dramatist, Pierre Corneille, and puts great stock in his children, even us girls, being properly read. I was lucky, therefore, to have received a convent education. Unlike most French girls of the late 1700s, I have read and discussed the ideas of today's leading thinkers: the Enlightenment philosophers. I agree with their call for immediate social and political change in France.

But Marat and his ilk pushed us too far. He had to be stopped.

Now because of my act – because I murdered a man – I, too, am condemned to die. This evening, 17 July 1793, I will be taken to the *Place de la Révolution* and beheaded at the guillotine, just as my king was. Just as I fear his Queen, Marie Antoinette, soon will be.

Before I die, I want you to know my story, for it is also the story of The French Revolution.

The Enlightenment

The Enlightenment was an intellectual movement of the 18th century (the 1700's) that originated in Europe, particularly in London and Paris. Enlightenment philosophers and writers were the first to question the "divine right of kings" – absolute monarchy – and the strict teachings of the Roman Catholic Church. They believed in the importance of the individual and they fought for the recognition of human rights, religious tolerance, freedom from censorship and the right to fair trial. They believed that governments should be run by the people through voting and representation, not by a king whose position was based solely on birth. Prominent French Enlightenment thinkers include Montesquieu (1689-1755), Voltaire (1694-1778), Jean-Jacques Rousseau (1712-1778) and Denis Diderot (1713-1784).

CHAPTER TWO

The Palais Royal

My tale starts 150 years before the French Revolution, at the meeting place between two of the finest palaces ever built in Paris: the *Palais du Louvre* and the Palais Royal. In 1789, few French people lived in such grand style. And in 1620, when the Palais Royal was first built, this level of luxury was known only to members of the royal family and persons of high birth or rank: the nobility.

The Palais Royal was originally the home of Cardinal de Richelieu, chief advisor to King Louis XIII (13th), and some say the real power behind the throne.

Cardinal de Richelieu

Cardinal de Richelieu built his beautiful home, which he called the Palais Cardinal, just across the street from the king, who lived at the *Palais du Louvre* at what was then the very edge of the city of Paris.

On 4 December 1642, Cardinal de Richelieu died. He left his palace to the king. But King Louis XIII never had a chance to use it for he died five months later.

His son and heir to the throne, Louis XIV (14th), was then only 4 years old, much too young to run a country.

So his mother, Anne of Austria, ruled as regent until he was old enough to take the crown. She didn't like the drafty then-300-year-old Louvre Palace, so she moved young King Louis and his little brother, Philippe, Duc d'Orleans, to the more modern Palais Cardinal. Because members of the royal family were now living in the palace, its name was changed to the Palais Royal.

On his 13th birthday, in 1652, Louis XIV declared himself King. (Can you imagine wanting to run a whole country when only 13?)

He moved back to the Louvre Palace, where he lived for 30 years. In 1682, he moved his family and the entire French government to Versailles.

KING LOUIS XIV

How old was Louis XIV when he declared himself king?

A. 4 years old

B. 13 years old

C. 17 years old

The Palais Royal remained the home of his younger brother, Philippe, Duc d'Orleans. It would stay in the hands of the Orleans branch of the royal family for the next 150 years. By 1789, the Palais Royal was home to Philippe's great-grandson, Louis-Philippe Joseph II, Duc d'Orleans. He was the first cousin of my king, Louis XVI.

Remember his name, for Louis-Philippe Joseph II, Duc d'Orleans, played a major role in fanning the flames that sparked the French Revolution.

King Louis XIV

CHAPTER THREE

France in 1789

French society at the time of my birth was distinctly out of balance. Four per-cent of the population – the royals, certain nobility, and the Church – held all the power and owned much of the wealth.

They gained their wealth by taxing the remaining 96% of us, those they called the Third Estate.

The People under the Ancien Régime

There was a time when the Third Estate comprised France's poorest members. But by 1789 the Third Estate included a growing class of wealthy businessmen and entrepreneurs called the bourgeoisie.

The bourgeoisie had no political power in France.

And they wanted it.

They wanted it because they felt the country, and their money, were being mismanaged by the crown. You see, the monarchy was fast running out of gold. Both Louis XIV and Louis XV (15th) spent more than 100 years fighting wars they did not win. More recently, the army of Louis XVI helped the American revolutionaries win their freedom from the British at great expense to France.

Yet while the poor had hardly enough money to buy bread after paying taxes to the king, the Church, and their noble landlords, the king and queen continued to enjoy a sumptuous lifestyle at the Palace of Versailles.

Ours was a society built on the backs of its poorest citizens. The Enlightenment thinkers, under threat of censorship and imprisonment, even execution, were the first to decry this relationship as unjust.

The bourgeoisie just refused to pay taxes, no longer wishing to support the court's lavish lifestyle.

And the poor grew more and more hungry. The hungrier they got, the angrier they became.

They could not be asked to pay more.

PUBLIC ART AT THE PALAIS ROYAL

Les Deux Plateaux (The Two Plateaus) by Daniel Buren was installed in the Cour d'Honneur of the Palais Royal in 1986 to cover up what had been an ugly car parking lot.

These twin sculptures, called Les Fontaines (The Fountains) by Op artist Pol Bury, were installed at the Palais Royal in 1970. Although they do not actually move, they are considered a fine example of Kinetic Minimalism. Can you see why?

English philanthropist Sir Richard Wallace introduced these public drinking fountains in the late 1870s. Called Wallace Fountains, 77 can still be found throughout the city of Paris. They continue to provide Paris with clean, potable water today. There are three at the Palais Royal.

François Arago was a French mathematician, physicist, astronomer, and ardent republican who grew up during the French Revolution. His achievements are remembered in a 1994 public installation by Jan Dibbets, called Hommage à Arago, in which the artist set 135 bronze medallions bearing Arago's name along the Paris meridian for a distance of 9.2 kms (5.7 miles). You can still find many in Paris today, including four at the Palais Royal.

The gardens of the Palais Royal are dotted with sculpture such as this one that dates to the era of King Louis XIV.

CHAPTER FOUR

Change Draws Near

Matters worsened terribly in the spring of 1789 when France's harvest was wiped out by a hailstorm. With grain scarce, the price of bread climbed so high that the poor could not feed themselves. By the summer of 1789, French peasants were starving and growing desperate.

Many sensed that the time for change was nigh.

Americans had recently overthrown their monarch in favor of a republican government, run by the people, for the people. More than 100 years before that, Britain had created a government ruled by the people in collaboration with the king: a constitutional monarchy.

Louis XVI Gives Alms

Even members of the French clergy and nobility felt it was time to overthrow the absolute monarchy that had ruled France for more than 800 years.

One such advocate for change was the king's cousin, Louis-Phillippe Joseph II, Duc d'Orleans. Being a royal, he was able to express his opinions openly. While most people were in danger of imprisonment or execution for expressing such treasonous views, members of the royal family were exempt, by royal edict, from censorship.

Louis-Philippe used this to his benefit, and to that of the coming Revolution.

Let me show you how...

INDIVIDUAL HUMAN RIGHTS

Louis-Philippe Joseph II, Duc d'Orleans, grew up in the Age of Enlightenment. He was greatly influenced by the importance of the individual in society. (He also wanted the king's job.) Which of the then-novel human rights listed below were NOT advocated by enlightenment philosophers?

A. Freedom of religious practice

B. Freedom of speech

C. Right to fair trial by jury

D. Equal rights for women and people of color

ANSWER: D

Part Two
REVOLUTION

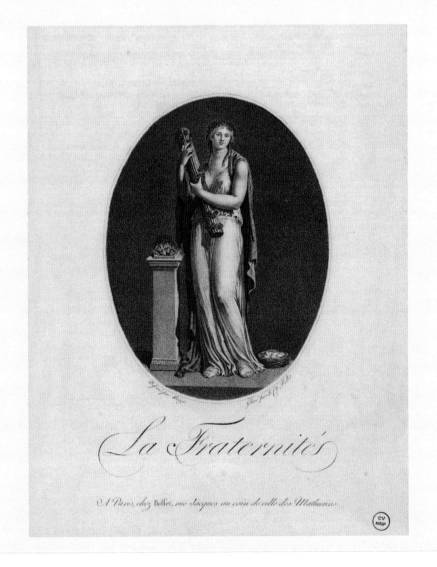

La Fraternité

A Paris, chez Bance, rue Jacques au coin de celle des Mathurins.

CHAPTER FIVE

Royal Hall to Public Mall

The gardens of the Palais Royal were for a long time private, enclosed by the backs of houses that faced the outer lying streets. Louis-Philippe Joseph II, Duc d'Orleans, changed that.

From 1781 to 1784, he turned his family's once-privileged domain into France's first-ever public shopping arcade. He transformed his personal palace gardens into a popular Parisian social center.

Truth is, the Duc d'Orleans, like his cousin the king, needed money. He was a notorious gambler and he squandered the Orleans' family fortune building a private pleasure garden to rival Queen Marie-Antoinette's hamlet at Versailles.

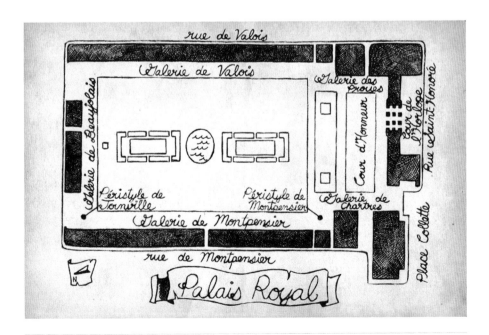

THE PALAIS ROYAL GARDEN

So, he built this new housing and shopping arcade around the perimeter of the Palais Royal gardens, and he did something that had never been done before in France: He sold or rented the apartment spaces to people from all levels of French society, with large apartments for the rich on the first level above the shops, and smaller, more affordable apartments as you reach the roof. He rented the gallery spaces to cafés, smart shops, theatres, restaurants, and even a few gambling casinos.

Louis-Philippe Joseph also encouraged printing presses to open here at the Palais Royal, presses that published and distributed journals and broadsheets expressing the Enlightenment views that were so unpopular with the king.

But because this was royal ground prior to the Revolution, the king's police were not permitted to enter the property. Therefore, neither Louis-Philippe nor those who printed revolutionary literature here could be censored under the monarchy.

It is thanks to these broadsheets that we in Normandy, and elsewhere in the French provinces, have been made aware of the events taking place in the French capital since 1789.

In a few short years, Louis-Philippe Joseph II, Duc d'Orleans, turned the Palais Royal into *the* place to be in Paris. Since their opening, these gardens have been crowded with people both day and night. I read in a popular journal printed at the Palais Royal that if you threw an apple from an apartment window it would never hit the ground – that's how thick the crowd can be!

Café tables and chairs spill out into the gardens at all hours. Circus acts and street performers entertain the crowds. Both Parisians as well as visitors from the provinces, like myself, come to the Palais Royal to shop, gamble, drink, and mingle, because this is the place to meet and discuss the ideas of Enlightenment philosophy. And where, in 1789, it was very fashionable to talk of Revolution.

That's why it is said that the French Revolution started here...

...at the Palais Royal.

GRAVEUR GUILLAUMOT

There is a business in the Palais Royal that opened in 1784. It is called the Graveur Guillaumot. Graveur translated into English means "engraver." How might this business have helped Louis-Philippe Joseph II and the revolutionary cause?

> **A.** It prepared food for the radical revolutionaries.
>
> **B.** Enlightenment thinkers slept here.
>
> **C.** It printed journals and broadsheets expounding revolutionary ideas.

ANSWER: C

CHAPTER SIX

What is a Revolution?

A revolution is a relatively sudden and drastic change in either the social, political, cultural, or economic institutions of a society. Some revolutions are led by the majority population of a nation; others are led by a small band of people who think radically differently from the rest. Some revolutions are peaceful; others are violent.

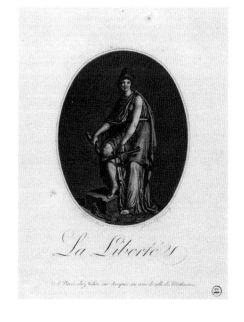

The French Revolution was all these things.

In 1789 it began peacefully, but quickly turned violent. It had the support, initially, of most French people, like me, and my nobleman father. But it was taken over in a few short years by the most radical extremists. People like Jean-Paul Marat, whose life I am guilty of taking, Georges Danton and Maximilien Robespierre, who in turn will soon take mine.

Simply put, the French revolution was the overthrow of the French government by the French governed.

Some believed that a republican government – one run by French citizens rather than an absolute monarch – was possible in France. Others felt that a constitutional monarchy would bring the greatest liberty, equality, and fraternity to all.

It had happened in England in 1689, and in the United States in 1776, with the help of French soldiers.

In 1789, it was France's turn for political and social change. It was France's turn for Liberty.

The Revolutionary Cannon

In 1786, the clock maker, Rousseau, whose shop was at the Palais Royal, placed his "Revolutionary Cannon" in the enclosed garden closest to the Cour d'Honneur. Legend has it that the cannon went off every day all by itself thanks to a magnifying glass positioned just above the fuse that was ignited by the rays of the noonday sun.

Rousseau's cannon worked for well more than 100 years, until 1914. In 1990, it was remodeled and has worked ever since.

An engraved message once on the side read: *I count only happy hours.*

CHAPTER SEVEN

Peaceful Revolution

To his credit, King Louis XVI recognized in the summer of 1789 that his country was in crisis. He called for a meeting of the Estates General – equal numbers of representatives from the nobility, clergy, and Third Estate – to help him resolve the situation.

No French King had convened the Estates General for over 150 years. So, new delegates to the counseling body had to be selected from all corners of the country.

In June, 12,000 delegates to the Estates General arrived at Versailles, each sporting the dress of their social class: The Third Estate wore plain

King Louis XVI

black suits and three corner hats. The nobility were bedecked in silks and plumes. The clergy shouldered their traditional vestments.

They came to help find a solution to France's financial problems. They came to usher in a new, golden age for France. They carried with them the hope and optimism of the entire French nation.

Confidence reigned.

But it quickly soured.

The Third Estate demanded more voting power. They did, after all, represent 96% of the French population. But they had only as many votes as the clergy and nobility, and these two always voted with the monarchy.

The demand of the Third Estate did not sit well with the king and his advisors.

He locked them out of the meeting.

THE TENNIS COURT OATH

Match the labels below with each of the three members of the Estates General among the central figures in this image by the painter Jacques-Louis David.

A. Clergy ____   **B.** Third-Estate ____   **C.** Noblemen ____

CHAPTER EIGHT

A New Constitution

With the hopes and dreams of the entire nation weighing heavily on their shoulders, the Third Estate refused to leave Versailles. They held their own meeting in the king's indoor games court, the *jeu de paume*, the only place big enough to accommodate their numbers and shelter them from the storm that raged like their fury with the old regime. They proclaimed themselves "the true representatives of the French people." They named themselves The National Assembly, an assembly not of the Estates, but of "The People." France's new government.

Forty-seven nobles and many clergy as well left the king's meeting to join the National Assembly, among them Louis-Philippe Joseph II, Duc d'Orleans. They pledged an oath to write France her first constitution.

It seemed the Revolution was won.

But King Louis XVI was not so quick to recognize France's new, self-proclaimed government.

Where did it put him? Where did it leave his son, the dauphin, the future King of France?

As he awaited the new constitution, he grew anxious of the rumble back in Paris. He sent troops to surround the city.

Parisians grew scared of the weapons now pointing at them.

THE TENNIS COURT OATH

Why did the members of the Third Estate hold their own meeting?

> **A.** There was no place big enough at Versailles to cater to all the guests.
>
> **B.** King Louis XVI, at the urging of his advisors, uninvited them to his meeting.
>
> **C.** The acoustics in the *jeu de paume* game courts made it easier to hear.
>
> **D.** They didn't feel the king's meeting was accomplishing anything new.

ANSWER: B

23

Part Three
VIOLENCE

CHAPTER NINE

The Mob Stirs

On 12 July 1789, while dining at one of the Palais Royal's most frequented cafés, the *Café des Foy*, Camille Desmoulins, a poor journalist from northeastern France and Third Estate representative to the Estates General, found himself surrounded by a shouting, angry mob, frightened by the advance of the king's troops on Paris. How would they defend themselves against the king's soldiers? What would they do if the troops were ordered to charge?

Desmoulins was known for his awkward stutter. But on this day he lost it, at least for a little while. If they needed weapons, they would steal them from the king! They would capture the king's munitions at *Les Invalides!*

Camille Desmoulins

He climbed up onto a table here at the *Café des Foy*, and shouted, *"Aux armes, citoyens!"* To arms, citizens! "Plunder the arsenal!"

In France, green is the color of hope. Desmoulins tore a green, leafy branch off a nearby tree and put it in his hat. The rowdy mob of people also tore tree branches to adorn their hats until they had stripped bare the trees of the Palais Royal. From that moment, wearing or waving a tree branch symbolized one's hope and support for the Revolution.

OTHER SYMBOLS OF THE FRENCH REVOLUTION

A. French Constitution A fundamental document of the 18th century, the Declaration of the Rights of Man and Citizen defined what came to be accepted as the natural, universal rights of the individual. It holds great importance, therefore, not only in French history but in the history of human rights.

B. Phrygian Cap Otherwise known as the Liberty cap, this conical bonnet was given to freed slaves in Roman times as a symbol of their liberty. The Paris revolutionaries wore a red cap of the same shape to signify the unification of all those against despotism and tyranny.

C. Fasces This image of a bundle of wooden sticks with a blade emerging from the center is Roman in origin. It was taken up by the French Revolutionaries to symbolize strength through unity.

D. Eye of Providence Usually associated with Freemasonry, this image represents the all-seeing eye and holder of divine knowledge.

E. The Cockade A cockade was a circular ribbon typical of the 18th century that was usually fastened to a man's hat. Its colors symbolized one's political beliefs. In Revolutionary France you wore a white cockade if you stood with the monarchy, a black cockade if you were against both monarchy and revolution, and a tricolor, red, white and blue, cockade if you supported Revolution.

CHAPTER TEN

Storm the Bastille!

On July 13, the morning after Citizen Desmoulins' speech, 60,000 people met at *Les Invalides*, the home for veterans of French wars. They got away with over 10 cannon and 28,000 muskets belonging to the king's army without any resistance from the troops on guard there. But, they found no gunpowder.

Oh, how I wished I had been there. My father forbade me to travel to Paris that summer. He said it was too dangerous. And he was probably right. For the next day, July 14, a mob even larger than the day before met at the *Bastille*, a 14th century fortress, turned prison.

The Awakening of the Third Estate.

Prise de la Bastille

The *Bastille* was enormous: eight stone towers linked 80-foot walls. The gunpowder needed to fuel the army's munitions was hiding there. The *Bastille* had long been associated with the worst abuses of the monarchy's power - torture, deprivation, unfair trial – and we French people hated it.

Armed with cannon and guns stolen from *Les Invalides,* as well as scythes, clubs, pikes, even stones – anything that could be used as a weapon – the mob demanded the fortress guards to give them gunpowder and to free their prisoners. The guards would not allow the mob inside and prepared to defend the *Bastille* with rooftop cannon.

No one knows who actually fired first. But after a standoff lasting many hours, a gun blast was suddenly heard. The mob, thinking it was under attack, stormed the fortress. Members of the new Revolutionary police force, the National Guard, joined them.

The mob chopped off the head of the *Bastille* guard and stuck it on a pike. His head, dripping with blood, was held high for all to see.

The people went wild, tearing the *Bastille* apart, stone by stone, until their fingers bled. They freed the prisoners being held there, surprised to find only seven. They stole the king's gunpowder to fuel the king's arms.

A violent, more radical Revolution was now upon us.

"Quatorze Juillet" not "Bastille Day"

July 14 was eventually declared France's official date of national celebration, *La Fête Nationale*, but not until 1880, 100 years after the French Revolution.

Mais Attention! Though the celebration is held on the anniversary of the storming of the *Bastille*, the French never refer to it as "Bastille Day."

They prefer the moniker, *Le Quatorze Juillet*, the 14th of July, with its less violent connotation.

CHAPTER ELEVEN

Louis XVI Consents

On July 17, King Louis XVI rushed to Paris. He stood on the balcony of the Hôtel de Ville before his subjects. He recognized the power of the National Assembly.

In addition to wearing his customary white – the color of the French Monarchy – he also wore red and blue – the colors of Paris. These three colors quickly became the colors of France's first republican flag: *le tricolore*.

With the king's blessing, the National Assembly got right to work to declare the new rights of all French citizens under the new French Republic. In

Le Tricolore

August, the Assembly gave France what many of us believe to be the most important document of the 18th century:

La Déclaration des droits de l'homme et du citoyen (The Declaration of the Rights of Man and Citizen).

For those of us with food in our cupboards, the publication of the Declaration fueled our optimism for the future of France. But those with no bread on the table and winter on its way wondered what good their new rights were in this new constitutional monarchy.

From the Declaration of the Rights of Man and Citizen

All men are created equal. No man shall hold Absolute or Divine rule over others.

Henceforth the inalienable (absolute) rights of the individual will include the rights to:
- liberty,
- property,
- security,
- resistance to oppression, and
- the rights to freedom of speech and freedom of the press.

It is upon a sovereign (self-governing) people on whom, henceforth:
- the law of the nation should rest,
- to whom officials should be responsible, and
- by whom finances should be controlled.

SYSTEMS OF GOVERNMENT

The ideals expressed in The Declaration form the basis of which of the following political system?

A. Monarchy

B. Dictatorship

C. Democratic Republic

ANSWER: C

CHAPTER TWELVE

March of Women

October 5: A mob of angry Parisian women assembled at the Palais Royal. From there, they began a full day's march to Versailles, on foot.

I read that Louis-Philippe Joseph II, Duc d'Orleans, the king's cousin, marched among them, dressed as a woman!

They went to Versailles to demand that King Louis XVI and Queen Marie Antoinette come to Paris to witness their hunger and poverty. They pleaded with Marie Antoinette to give them bread to help them feed their children. A rumor spread that when the queen was told the women had no bread, she replied, "Then, let them eat cake!" This made the women very angry.

October March of Women

"Let them eat cake!"

For more than two centuries it has often been said that Marie Antoinette spoke those words on the evening of the October March of Women, 5 October 1789. She never did. This phrase was first uttered by another French queen, the Spanish Infata, Maria Teresa, wife of King Louis XIV, more than 100 years before the French Revolution began. The words were falsely attributed to Marie Antoinette during the Revolution to make her look bad in the eyes of the hungry people.

The women stood waiting well into the night. In the pre-dawn hours, they broke into the palace. They made for the queen's bedchamber. But she escaped through the servants' passageways within the palace walls. They sacked Marie Antoinette's rooms, breaking or stealing its precious contents.

The National Guard joined the women, beheading anyone who blocked the furies' path.

The women refused to leave Versailles unless the royal family left with them. By morning, they were victorious.

On October 6, the king and queen, their two living children, and the king's sister, Madame Elizabeth, were prisoners of the mob, en route in a crowded carriage to Paris.

Their 12-hour parade to the Tuileries Palace left a trail of blood as the women held the heads of the king's troops on pikes. They waved green tree branches as a symbol of the revolution.

The royal family would never see Versailles again.

The Life and Death of
Queen Marie Antoinette's Children

Before the start of the French Revolution in 1789, Marie Antoinette had already lost two of her four children. Her youngest, Sophie-Beatrix, died shortly before her first birthday in 1787. The painting shown below by Louise Elizabeth Vigée Lebrun, was begun before the baby died. Thus the artist had to paint the young babe out of the picture. Soon after, the queen's eldest son and heir to the throne, Louis-Joseph, shown here pointing into the empty cradle, was diagnosed with spinal tuberculosis. He died just one month before the meeting of the Estates General at Versailles. The summer of 1789 was not a happy time for the King and Queen of France.

Part Four

WAR

Mitglieder der Kommune. (1793—1794.)

CHAPTER THIRTEEN

Attempted Escape!

One June night in 1791, after more than a year-and-a-half under virtual house arrest in the Tuileries Palace, King Louis XVI and his family dressed up as servants and stole away, one by one, under cover of night. Together in a large green and black carriage, fitted with a white velvet interior, food enough, a retractable table and other conveniences of home, they headed north-east to France's border with the Austrian Empire. Waiting to help them just outside France were troops assembled by the queen's brother, King Leopold II of Austria, as well as the King of Prussia.

Louis XVI Stopt

But things went terribly wrong. They were delayed en route and so missed the escorts that were arranged to accompany them to the border. When the sun rose over the Tuilieries Palace, the royal family was discovered missing. Word quickly reached us in the provinces that the king and his family were on the run. National Guardsmen were dispatched in all directions to find them.

I prayed for their safe escape. But a small town postmaster near the border of the Austrian Empire recognized the king when he briefly put his head out of the carriage. Despite his disguise, the king was easily recognizable for his profile was printed on all French coins.

The postmaster rode on ahead to the next town, Varenne. When the king and his family arrived there, the National Guard was waiting to arrest them. The Guard escorted the king and his family back to Paris and placed them under strict house arrest once again.

So frightened was the queen that upon their return her hair had turned completely white.

Louis XVI Coin

FLIGHT TO VARENNES

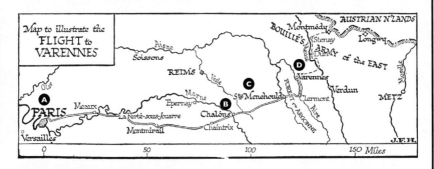

A. Paris The royal escape began in Paris from the Tuileries Palace, which no longer exists.

B. Chalons The royal family first met trouble in Chalons where the soldiers meant to escort them to the border were nowhere to be found.

C. Sainte-Menehould Not far from Chalons, in St-Menehould, King Louis XVI was spotted by the Post-Master Jean-Baptiste Drouet.

D. Varennes And just a bit further on, in Varennes, the royal family was stopped, captured, and escorted back to Paris.

CHAPTER FOURTEEN

Fractured Revolution

At that point, the revolution took a radical turn to the left. Many French lost complete faith in their king after his attempt to flee France. Those who stood with the monarchy, the Royalists, left France for good. The moderate Constitutional Monarchists, called *Girondins*, began to lose control of the National Assembly as their delegates defected to the revolutionary left on the side of the *Jacobins*.

The *Jacobins* took over the National Assembly, creating a new government they called the National Convention. With the radical *Jacobin*,

Philippe Egalité

George Danton, in the lead, the National Convention abolished the monarchy and the Church, just like that.

Louis-Philippe, Duc d'Orleans, one of few royals left in France, was a known *Girondin* sympathizer. As politics in Paris grew more radical, he grew scared.

To prove his commitment to the Revolution, he changed his name to *Philippe-Egalité* (Philip Equality); he renamed the Palais Royal, the *Palais Egalité* (Equality Palace); and he baptized the *Palais Egalité* grounds, the *Jardin Egalité* (Equality Garden).

Perhaps he would have fled France as well if he knew what was yet to come.

Political Labels

Have you noticed that political parties are labeled based on whether their views are considered to be to the left, center, or right?

Did you know that this tradition began in France during the Revolution?

It all started when the radical delegates of the National Assembly sat themselves together on the left side of the Assembly President. The moderate *Girondins* sat in the middle, in front of the President, while the conservative Royalists congregated to the President's right.

As the Revolution gained radical momentum, the Royalists fled and many moderates became radicalized. Now dominant, the leftists dissolved the National Assembly and established the more extreme National Convention. There were so many radical delegates to the Convention that they were obliged to sit higher and higher in the meeting hall, once the equestrian facility of the Tuileries Palace. They became known as "The Mountain," which described them both literally and figuratively, in contrast to "The Plain," whose moderate delegates became so few that they barely filled the Convention floor.

POLITICAL LABELS

The *Jacobins* were members of "The Mountain" and can be said to belong on which side of the political spectrum?

   A. The radical left

   B. The moderate center

   C. The conservative right

ANSWER: A

CHAPTER FIFTEEN

Reign of Terror

If you're not already seated, you may want to be, for the next part of my tale may be difficult to comprehend and even more difficult to believe.

The Church now abolished, all convents and monasteries were suppressed. My sister and I were therefore obliged to leave our convent school. I moved into the home of an old family friend in Caen, a city near the Normandy coast. There, I followed the course of the Revolution with feverish interest, devouring whatever political pamphlets and news from Paris came my way.

In April of 1792, Austria and Prussia declared war on France. I was glad. The moderate *Girondins*, with whom I sided, hoped a war would put an end to the *Jacobin* revolt and enable a constitutional monarchy to return to France.

Siege of the Tuileries

THE SACKING OF THE TUILERIES

Why didn't King Louis XVI's royal guards fight back when they were attacked?

A. They lacked weapons.

B. They didn't know how.

C. They had received royal orders to bring no harm to the people.

It did not. The *Jacobins* had other plans.

In August the *Jacobins* proclaimed Georges Danton Minister of Justice, making him the dictator of Paris. At his side were Camille Desmoulins and Maximilien Robespierre.

All three had the support of Jean-Paul Marat who, through his paper, *Ami du Peuple* (Friend of the People), painted 'Louis and Antoinette' as enemies of the people.

To strike a final blow to the French Monarchy, Danton and his *Jacobin* friends encouraged the people to attack the Tuileries Palace where the king and his family lived under house arrest. The royal family escaped out the back of the Palace with just enough time to spare for the King Louis XVI to give his last orders to the royal guards: He forbade them from drawing arms on the rioting civilians.

The siege was awful! In only two hours the rabble succeeded in killing and mutilating the king's defenseless guards, whose severed heads and bloody remains were tossed everywhere.

Paris became an *abbatoir*, a slaughterhouse.

As the mob plundered the Palace the royal family fled to the National Convention, housed in the equestrian facility of the Tuileries. There, they ran right into the hands of the radical *Jacobins*, who immediately arrested the king and queen, accused them of collaborating with the Austrian and Prussian armies, and sent them to the Temple fortress, yet another wretched medieval prison.

La Marseillaise
The French National Anthem

One April evening in 1792, Claude-Joseph Rouget de Lisle, amateur musician and officer in France's Revolutionary Army, penned the words to a rousing tune meant to help rally volunteers to defend their fatherland against Austrian and Prussian forces. The song caught on and eventually found its way south to Marseilles where it was played at a patriotic banquet in honor of the troops from that region. Copies of the song were passed around so the volunteers might sing along. In August of that year, the same men marched into Paris singing the song they learned that night. They would play a major role in the 10 August sacking of the Tuileries that resulted in the arrest and imprisonment of the royal family. Although originally entitled *Chant de guerre de l'armeé du Rhin* (War Song of the Army of the Rhine), the song became known as *La Marseillaise* because of its popularity with the soldiers from that region.

On 14 July 1795, the National Convention decreed that *La Marseillaise* be adopted as France's national anthem. After the Revolution, the song would be banned throughout most of the 19th century due to its violent connotations. However, it was never forgotten and emerged again as the French national anthem in 1879. Here is the first verse and chorus, with an English translation:

Allons enfants de la Patrie,	Let us go, children of the fatherland
Le jour de gloire est arrivé !	Our day of Glory has arrived!
Contre nous, de la tyrannie,	Against us stands tyranny,
L'étandard sanglant est levé,	The bloody flag is raised,
L'étandard sanglant est levé,	The bloody flag is raised.
Entendez-vous, dans la campagnes.	Do you hear in the countryside,
Mugir ces farouches soldats ?	The roar of these savage soldiers?
Ils viennent jusque dans vos bras	They're coming right into your arms
Égorger vos fils, vos compagnes !	To cut the throats of your sons, your companions.
Aux armes citoyens !	To arms, citizens!
Formez vos bataillons,	Form your battalions,
Marchons, marchons !	March on, march on!
Qu'un sang impur	Until their impure blood
Abreuve nos sillons.	Waters the furrows in our fields.

CHAPTER SIXTEEN

September Massacres

I wish I could tell you that the violence stopped there. But it only served to quicken Marat's thirst for blood. As Prussian troops crossed the French border and began their advance on Paris, Marat called on France to rid herself of all "revolutionary traitors." By that he meant all the nobles, clergy, and moderate bourgeoisie who had waited too long to flee. He advocated that they be killed before they could join forces with the invading Prussian and Austrian armies. All moderate Girondins and Royalists still walking free were immediately rounded up and thrown into prison alongside those already being held.

The September Massacres

On 12 September 1792, groups of armed citizens gathered outside prisons all over the country. Frenzy ensued. Prisons were attacked. Prisoners were dragged out of the cells. Throughout the nation, people innocent of any real crime – even children – were butchered, their bodies left to rot in the streets.

George Danton

For four days, Danton allowed the butchery to continue with Marat laughing over his shoulder. They created terror among us. We no longer knew whom we could trust. They would, in turn, use our fear as a weapon against us.

They ruled us by terror.

On September 21, town criers proclaimed throughout the streets of Paris that the National Convention now ruled France's first Republic.

Then, in December, 1792, the unthinkable happened...

The Republican Calendar

Republican Calendar

When the *Jacobins* took control of the National Convention, they attempted to wipe out all systems that could be associated with the former monarchy, the *Ancien Régime,* or with the Catholic Church, such as the seven-day week starting and ending on the day of prayer. The *Jacobins* sought to base their new systems either in nature, or in multiples of 10, and using only latinate names. One example of these efforts is the Republican Calendar.

The first day of France's republican era began the day after the National Convention abolished the monarchy on 21 September 1792. That's when use of the Republican Calendar began. The calendar was made up of twelve months, three months for each season. Republican months were divided into three ten-day weeks.

The names of the Republican months used Latin words to describe the natural conditions corresponding to that time. The three months of winter, for example, were named: Nivôse, meaning snowy; Pluvôse, or rainy; and Ventôse, for windy.

This prompted English critics to mock the calendar by calling the months: Wheezy, Sneezy, and Freezy; Slippy, Drippy, and Nippy; Showery, Flowery, and Bowery; Wheaty, Heaty, and Sweety.

Republican days were divided into 10 hours, each with 100 minutes that were further divided into 100 seconds, making the Republican hour almost twice as long as a conventional hour. Clocks were manufactured to reflect this use of decimal time, but the system never really caught on.

After the equivalent of about 12 conventional calendar years, Emperor Napoleon Bonaparte finally did away with the Republican Calendar on 1 January 1806.

Part Five
MURDER

CHAPTER SEVENTEEN

Death Sentence

The National Convention denounced King Louis XVI, France's king – my king – as an "enemy of the Revolution"

He was separated from his family and taken before the Convention on 11 December 1792.

In a matter of days, my king was tried, convicted of treason, and sentenced to death by guillotine.

Exuberant Executioner

All the Jacobin delegates to the National Convention voted to kill him. Among the *Girondin* delegates, 21 voted against. The vote for execution was signed by Philippe-Egalité, the king's own cousin!

On 21 January 1793, King Louis XVI lost his head on the *Place de la Révolution.*

I read in a Paris journal that 80,000 people crowded onto the *Place* to watch the execution of the king. To make room for this number people, a statue of his grandfather, Louis XV, was torn down and the guillotine placed on the platform near where the statue once stood.

Louis XVI was the last of France's absolute monarchs.

Before the King was cold in his grave, Danton, Marat, Desmoulins, and Robespierre turned on the 21 *Girondins* delegates who had voted to spare the king. They accused them of "crimes against the Revolutionary cause." Eighteen of them fled Paris together. They came to Caen, where I was then living.

I met them frequently at their lodgings.

I plucked from them every detail possible about the trial of the king and the events taking place in Paris.

I brought them journals and pamphlets that made their way to Normandy.

I became their friend.

HISTORIC CAEN, NORMANDY

Caen is a city on the English Channel in Normandy, a region that looms large in the history of France. The city is located just west of Rouen and dates to the time of William the Conqueror, the first Norman King of England. He reigned from 1066 until his death in 1087.

Nine-hundred years later, from June-August 1944, Caen was the site of heavy fighting between Allied and German forces in World War II. The Battle for Caen was part of the greater Battle for Normandy that commenced on 6 June 1944 with the D-Day landings on the nearby beaches and would eventually lead to the defeat of the Nazis.

During the French Revolution, in 1792, 18 of the 21 Girondin delegates to the National Convention fled to Caen after their attempt to save King Louis XVI from the guillotine. They were hidden and protected there by others sympathetic to their political point of view.

CHAPTER EIGHTEEN

Marat's Murder

Like my *Girondin* friends, I read about the sham trial and condemnation of my king in Marat's ill-named journal, *Ami du people,* or Friend of the People. Marat made no secret of his views. He was thrilled at the death-sentence leveled at my king. He demanded that the National Convention also find and sever the heads of the 21 *Girondin* delegates who had attempted to save poor "Louis the Last."

I believed then, as I do now, that Marat, with his hateful *Jacobin* opinions, was the cause of the Reign of Terror now gripping my country.

Jean-Paul Marat

He was responsible for the desecration of the churches. He was to blame for the savage deaths of priests and nobles massacred in their prison cells. It is because of him that friend now denounces friend and neighbor denounces neighbor, all in an attempt to save their own necks.

Because of Marat, we all live in fear; we are ruled by terror. Heads roll by the hundreds from the guillotines; their blades and the streets beneath them stained a perpetual blood red. Marat encouraged it all to happen through his ill-named journal, Friend of the People. *He had to be stopped.*

I decided to do it myself. I would sacrifice my life to save France and my *Girondin* compatriots, to avenge my king and the peaceful Revolution. The moderate *Girondin* are the true saviors of France. I had to kill Marat to stop them from being killed. This would be my contribution to creating a lasting peace in France.

On 9 July 1793, I bade farewell to my childhood home after seeing all my friends and settling all my debts. I sent a note to my father telling him that I was leaving France for England, never to return. I begged his forgiveness that I did not call on him directly. I told him I was afraid that if I saw him again I would change my mind. I asked him to kiss my beloved sister for me. I gave my favorite sketchbook and pencils to the carpenter's boy on the corner.

I caught the coach to Paris, not daring to look back.

Charlotte in Caen

I arrived here in Paris two days later, on July 11, and secured room no. 7 at the *Hôtel de la Providence*, a small room on the 1st floor with a window facing the street.

I went directly to the *Palais Egalité* to learn the latest political news and to find out what I could of Marat's habits.

Before the sun had set on July 12, I knew that Marat no longer went to the Convention. He was ill, I discovered, and rarely left his home. I resolved to find him there, though I had hoped to cut him down on the Convention floor.

At 6:00 on the morning of July 13, I left my hotel. I found my way back to the *Palais Egalité* before the shops had opened for the day.

I walked slowly through the gardens one last time, with its rows of trees, green and cool in the clear morning air. I enjoyed the sounds of the city waking to a new day. The day dawned fresh. Birds sang with the advance of the sun. How bittersweet were those last moments of freedom.

By 8:00 the shops began to open, and I slipped into a cutler there at 177, *Galerie de Valois*. I bought a large knife for the cost of two francs. With the knife concealed in the bodice of my dress, I left the gardens at 9:00, resolved to track down the man I believed to be the murderer of the ideals of the French Revolution. I left in search of Jean-Paul Marat.

Follow me on the journey to end Marat's life…

…and mine.

MARAT'S PAPER

In your opinion, Marat's paper, *L'Ami du peuple*, would be best described as:

    A. Journalism

    B. Political Propaganda

    C. Satire

ANSWER: B

CHAPTER NINETEEN

Marat's Bath

It did not take me long to find the printing press where, until three days ago, on 13 July 1793 – until I killed him – Marat printed his revolutionary paper, Friend of the People. On an adjacent street, in an old house with a corner turret, Marat lived with his constant and faithful companion, Simone.

Detail from: Death of Marat

While at the *Palais Egalité*, I learned that I was not the only person who hated Marat. Indeed, he had many dangerous enemies as a result of the views expressed in his journal. He often had to go into hiding to keep from being killed. One such time he took refuge in the Paris sewers. While there, he contracted a terrible skin disease.

After that his only comfort was soaking in a tub of cold water and medicinal herbs. On his worst days, when the pain was very great, he stayed in his bath all day. On the evening of July 13, I found Marat thus, in the bath at his apartment around the corner from his press.

It was my third visit to his house that day. The first two times – once in the early morning, then at mid-day – I had been turned away by Simone. This time, however, I succeeded in gaining entry. I climbed the steps to Marat's door, one heavy foot at a time, and plucked up the courage to knock yet again.

I was confronted once more by a scowling and suspicious Simone, but before she could dismiss me a third time, I offered her, with a slightly trembling hand, a letter addressed to Monsieur Marat.

I had written the letter myself, in the heat of the afternoon after my second failed attempt to cross his threshold. The letter stated that I had come to name names; that I was prepared to give him information regarding the missing *Girondin* "enemies of the Revolution" that he sought.

Who would suspect a 24-year old girl?

Detail from: Death of Marat

Simone took the letter and shut the door with a slam, leaving me alone on that drab, inhospitable landing. I could have turned around right there and then. But Marat was just on the other side of that door. I took a long, deep breath, and held it. Would I again be turned away? If so, so be it. Or would I meet the monster Marat at last?

I met my enemy in a small, square room with a brick-tiled floor. A map of France hung upon worn wallpaper. His tub was the shape of a sabot, an old wooden shoe. A board lying across it served as a writing table so that Marat could work on his articles and conduct his interviews even while soaking.

To keep warm, he sat upon a linen sheet, the dry ends covering his bare shoulders. A second sheet, draped across the tub and writing table, offered him a bit of privacy from his visitors.

Marat was strange and unpleasant, thin and feverish. His head was wrapped in a filthy, vinegar-soaked handkerchief. On his skin were open lesions that reeked of decaying, rotten flesh. My eyes began to tear, struggling so against the fumes of death and medicine that I did not at first notice Marat motioning me to take the chair placed beside his bath.

I sat as requested, my head turned toward the window, searching the still, hot summer air for what little breeze might chance to come my way.

And in the gloom of evening's waning light, Marat took great pleasure in scribbling down one by one, his head bent over his writing table, the names of each of my beloved *Girondin* friends.

Once finished he raised his head, his blood-shot eyes met mine for the first time. He proclaimed viciously, hate dripping from his lips, "We'll soon have them all guillotined in Paris!"

At that moment I knew I had justly come. I pulled out my knife and stabbed Marat right through the heart.

One blow was all it took. I felt the knife penetrate flesh, bone, muscle.

It was shocking how easy it was.

Marat died almost instantly.

The Death of Marat

CHARLOTTE CORDAY IN ART HISTORY

Robert-Fleury, Tony (1838-1911). Charlotte Corday at Caen in 1793. Photo: R.G. Ojeda. Musée Bonnat, Bayonne, France. Photo Credit: Réunion des Musées Nationaux / Art Resource, NY.

Baudry, Paul (1828-1886). Charlotte Corday. 1860. Photo: Gérard Blot. Musée des Beaux-Arts, Nantes, France. Photo Credit: Réunion des Musées Nationaux / Art Resource, NY.

Charlotte Corday. Original steel engraving drawn by A. Lacauchie, engraved by Roze, 1849. Digital image courtesy of www.antique-prints.de.

Hauer, Jean Jacques (1751-1829). Charlotte Corday (1768-1793), 1793, Assassin of Marat as prisoner at the Conciergerie. Chateaux de Versailles et de Trianon, Versailles, France. Photo Credit: Réunion des Musées Nationaux / Art Resource, NY.

Charlotte Corday. From Evert A. Duykinck. A Portrait Gallery of Eminent Men and Women of Europe and America, with Biographies. New York: Johnson, Wilson, and Company, 1873. Digital image courtesy of the James Smith Noel Collection, Louisiana State University, Shreveport, LA.

Fournier, Mme., after Raffet. Charlotte on the Evening of Her Death, 1847, Lamartine's l'Histoire des Girondins (Furne and W. Coquebert), vol. 6, engraving facing page 264. Photographic reproduction courtesy Moby's Newt © 2010.

Part Six
PRISON

CHAPTER TWENTY

My Capture

As Simone and others rushed to Marat, I escaped into an antechamber. But I was immediately apprehended, my ears deafened by the wails of "Help!" and "Assassin!"

Someone hit me with a chair. I fell to the floor. Someone else tied my wrists together with a rough rope. It hurt terribly, but I didn't resist. I knew all along that it would come to this; I knew that killing Marat was as good as committing suicide.

I was questioned for hours, always the same demand. My interrogators wanted to know who was behind my act; who were my collaborators.

Over and over I told them it was my idea; that I acted alone.

It wasn't until midnight that was I placed in a coach and taken to the nearest prison. Though located close to Marat's apartments, it took two hours to reach it, for a huge crowd had gathered wishing to see the murderess of Jean-Paul Marat.

They menaced the horse and carriage, hurling death threats through distorted faces. I was frightened. I thought the people might tear me to pieces.

Charlotte Bound

This was not what I had expected. I thought they would rejoice. I thought they would carry me through the streets on their shoulders. Instead, they called me an "enemy of the Revolution."

Yesterday, I was transferred to the *Conciergerie*, the Revolutionary Prison, where most people these days leave by tumbrel – an open wooden cart used to ferry the condemned to their beheading at the *Place de la Révolution*. For this reason the *Conciergerie* is known today as "the antechamber to the guillotine."

I beg you to come visit me at the *Conciergerie* Prison, to bear witness to the conditions of my incarceration.

La Conciergerie

The *Conciergerie* is the jail attached to the *Palais de la Cité,* the first palace of the French Monarchy. In Roman times, the governor of Lutecia (as Paris was then called) built a fortress on the site where the *Palais de la Cité* now stands. Centuries later, in the year 987, the first of the French Kings, Hugh Capet, had the old fort enlarged and improved. For four hundred years the *Palais de la Cité* was the royal residence of the Kings of France. Over time it was modernized and renovated. In the 14th century, it was considered the most magnificent palace in all of Europe.

In 1364, King Charles V moved the French royal residence to the outskirts of the city. He converted an existing 12th century defense fortification, called the *Louvre,* into a small, private palace in order to escape the crowds, foul smells, and bad traffic on the *Ile de la Cité.* From that time forward, the *Palais de la Cité* took on a more administrative function for the king: He received visiting dignitaries there; he presided over his government – the Parlement – at the *Palais de la Cité;* and established the French Court of Law, where persons accused of breaking the laws were judged.

Now, every court of law requires a jail, and every jail requires a jailer. The *Conciergerie* was just that place – the court prison – so named because it was run by *Le Concierge,* as the jailer was then called. The Concierge lived there and held extensive powers over the prisoners. As prisoners then were considered guilty until proven innocent, they actually had to pay the Concierge for their stay in his prison.

By the 15th century (the 1400s), the *Conciergerie* was one of the largest prisons in Paris. The prison cells occupied the lower parts of the palace, and one of the four towers, the *Tour Bonbec,* was said to be a torture chamber.

Incarceration at the *Conciergerie* was usually temporary. After sentencing, the prisoner was either set free or incarcerated elsewhere – such as in the *Bastille* fortress – or executed at the *Place de Grève,* once just across the river near what is now the *Hôtel de Ville* (City Hall).

CHAPTER TWENTY ONE

My Trial

Four months before I killed Jean-Paul Marat, in March of 1793, the radical National Convention took over the *Conciergerie* and installed its own revolutionary court, called the *Tribunal.* Since then, the *Tribunal* has met in the great vaulted halls of the *Palais de Justice.*

On 15 July 1793, two days after killing Marat, my case was given to the dreaded Public Prosecutor and *Jacobin* sympathizer, Antoine Quentin Fouquier-Tinville. Yesterday, July 16, I was brought to the *Conciergerie* by his order.

Antoine Quentin Fouquier-Tinville

My ordeal here began with pre-trial questioning. I freely admitted to my act of murder. I insisted again on the truth: that I acted alone. I stated that I had killed not a man, but a savage beast that was devouring all of France; that I had killed one man to give peace to many.

With that Fouquier-Tinville immediately placed me in the *Conciergerie* Prison. My belongings were gathered from no. 7, *Hôtel de la Providence* and brought to me. I spent the day writing letters of farewell to my friends and family and cleaning my clothes in the prisoners' shared fountain for what I knew would be a swift trial. If I am going to die, it will be in dignity in a freshly laundered tunic, not in one stained with a madman's blood.

My trial was set for 8:00 this morning, 17 July 1793. I was brought into the vaulted hall a free citizen, my hands untied. I stood calmly before Antoine Quentin Fouquier-Tinville, and his fellow *Jacobin*, Maximilien Robespierre.

They were both friends of Marat. They sat beneath a statue of "Justice" amongst the five judges of the Revolutionary Tribunal. All of them were dressed in black with tricolor sashes and tall hats plumed with ostrich feathers. These ridiculous and dangerous men wasted no time deciding my fate.

Today, in only a matter of hours, I will die by the guillotine. Until then, as the painter Hauer sketches my portrait, I write this memoir to you, good citizens, to ask that all true Friends of Peace remember me.

History of the Guillotine

In 1789 the new Republican government of France, the National Assembly, adopted execution by guillotine. Invented by Dr. Joseph-Ignace Guillotin, the guillotine was thought to be a more humane form of execution, swifter than either hanging or drawing and quartering (pulling a person apart, limb-by-limb, by attaching each arm and each leg to one of four horses and urging all four horses to advance at the same time).

Another benefit of the guillotine was that it could be easily transported, so that executions could take place all over Paris.

During the Reign of Terror (from 1793 to 1795), execution by guillotine became commonplace. By June 1794, Paris saw an average of 36 guillotine executions per day. Executions took place in public areas so that the people could have the satisfaction of seeing the "guilty" punished. It became a form of public entertainment.

As many as 20,000 people lost their heads during the Reign of Terror.

THE CONCIERGERIE TOWERS

A. Tour Horloge — *The Clock Tower.* The original clock installed in this tower dated to around 1350. It was France's first public clock. It told the time for the entire City of Paris, then settled on the Ile de la Cité and the Latin Quarter to the south. The clock here now took the place of its predecessor in 1585.

B. Tour de Caesar — *Caesar's Tower.* This tower was named in memory of the Roman Emperor, Julius Caesar, whose writings make reference to Lutecia, as Paris was called under the Romans.

C. Tour d'Argent — *Silver Tower or Treasury Tower.* This is where the Kings of France stored their royal treasure.

D. Tour Bonbec — *Good Beak Tower.* This tower was the torture chamber of the medieval kings, where the accused "sang" (that is to say, he opened his mouth, or beak, to speak his confession) after being asked a "good question" (a euphemism for "just the right amount of torture").

CHAPTER TWENTY TWO

My Incarceration

Upon my arrival at the prison of the *Conciergerie,* I was first brought to the office of *Le Greffier,* the Clerk. He asked me many questions: my name, my profession, where I came from, my date of birth. He then very carefully wrote up a physical description of my person, a sort of verbal drawing. He read it aloud to see if I agreed with his observation. I said I did. It was really quite accurate.

Le Greffier then inscribed the date of my arrival at the *Conciergerie,* and the nature of my crime – murder. He asked me my motive. I told him proudly that I killed Jean-Paul Marat to save the Revolution.

Le Greffier

He looked up at me. He stared deeply into my eyes. His gaze fixed upon mine and lingered for some moments. I shuddered. Did he hate me? Was he grateful? Would my fellow citizens understand my sacrifice, after all? Would my father and dear sister ever forgive me?

I was then taken to meet Mr. Richard, my jailer, *Le Concierge*. He was kind to me. He knew I was soon to die. He asked me if I had any means, any money, to be a *pistole*, a prisoner able to afford a private or semi-private prison cell with a bed.

I said I had none. I had only brought along with me enough money to pay for my weapon: the knife I used to kill Marat.

And so I spent the last night of my life in a windowless prison cell, crowded in among the other *pailleux*, those able only to afford *paille*, or straw, for their last bed.

~~~

En route to the prison cells, we passed by the grooming room, *la salle de la toilette*. Sounds comforting, *n'est-ce pas?*, like a place to go to have the straw combed out of your hair?

Well, this is the last place we prisoners of the Revolution wish to be taken, for it is the last place we will all visit before our trip to the guillotine. You see, shortly before each of us is to die we are first brought here to have our hair cut above our necks.

Why, you ask? Because the only thing capable of slowing the guillotine blade is human hair. And that can only result in excruciating pain for the condemned.

We are meant to tip the barber, to thank him for the great care he takes with these preparations. But, alas, I had no more *pistole* to leave on his table.

~~~

The straw in my cell – in all the cells of the *pailleux*, I'm told – is changed only once each month. The prison of the *Conciergerie* is so grossly overcrowded that cells meant for four people are packed to 16 or 18.

It's dreadful in here, dark, always, even during the day.

La Salle de la Toilette

The walls sweat with damp from the foul-smelling River Seine which is known to overflow its banks in times of heavy rain.

We have only a shared bucket in case of necessity, and have no choice but to take turns sitting or lying down. It's impossible to sleep in these conditions, a reality made worse by the guards' constant banging on the metal grills of the prison's doors. Fear prevails in the *Conciergerie*, invading one's every sense.

Les pistoles and *prisoniers des marques*, those with their own cells, have enough money to bring in their books and beds. These are never provided by our jailer, *Le Concierge*, but are brought into the prison from the prisoner's own home.

Les prisoniers des marques spend their last days gorging on good food and wine, drinking and stuffing themselves with fare from the finest area restaurants, enjoying their last moments before their final journey to meet their maker.

~~~

While forced into our cramped cells by night, by day, we *pailleux* are allowed to wander the Prisoner's Gallery and visit the outdoor men's and women's courtyards. It is in the *Cour des Femmes*, the Women's Courtyard, where we women

WOMEN'S COURTYARD

A. Water Fountain The sole water source for the women prisoners of the *Conciergerie*.

B. Carré des douze On the day of their death, prisoners of the Revolution were held behind these iron gates, in groups of 12.

C. Death Bell This bell, sounded from the *Cour du Mai*, tolled the coming of the tumbrel, and the guillotine, for the next 12 victims of Mme la Guillotine.

D. Cour du Mai passage Prisoners were escorted through this passageway from the *Conciergerie* prison to the *Cour du Mai* and the tumbrel waiting just beyond.

prisoners of the *Conciergerie* under the French Revolution spend each long day leading up to our execution.

There, to the left, is our collective water fountain. It is here where we are permitted to bathe and wash out our clothes each morning.

Straight on and to the right, behind the iron gate, is a small, triangular courtyard, the *carré des douze,* where we prisoners are taken and held on the day of our execution, 12 at a time.

That's how many fit in a tumbrel.

When the tumbrel arrives to take us to the *Place de la Révolution,* the large bell above the *carré des douze* is sounded from a pull chain in the *Cour du Mai* (May Courtyard). It is also this bell that signals our return to the cells each night.

It is this bell that regulates life in the *Conciergerie.*

I've never hated a single object more.

~~~

At the end of the garden is a stone table where we women take turns eating our meager meals of water and bread.

It is upon this table that I write to you now.

Please join me there to hear the end of my tale...

La Chapelle des Girondins

In medieval times, when the *Conciergerie* was part of the royal *Palais de la Cité*, there existed a chapel. During the French Revolution, after the National Convention had abolished the Catholic Church, the chapel was no longer recognized as a sacred space. It was used as a prison cell instead.

After the Revolution, when the Church was allowed to function again in France, the chapel was renamed the *Chapelle des Girondins* to honor the 21 *Girondin* delegates to the Convention who had voted to spare King Louis XVI. Unfortunately, Marat's wish to kill these men was granted by Robespierre and Fouquier-Tinville. The 21 *Girondins* were labeled "Enemies of the Revolution" and brought here on 29 October 1793. They spent the night together in this chapel-turned-prison-cell before being taken to the guillotine and executed, one-by-one, on October 30.

This Chapel is also where Maximillien Robespierre spent his final hours. By 1794, French people had tired of the daily executions. It is said that the streets of Paris under the guillotines were then stained a permanent red. The arrest of Robespierre was demanded. When they came for him, he tried to shoot himself, but succeeded only in shattering his jaw. He was brought here, wounded, to recuperate before meeting the guillotine blade, himself, on 28 July 1794.

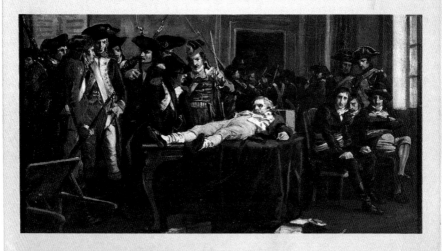

Part Seven

BEWARE MME LA GUILLOTINE

CHAPTER TWENTY THREE

The End

Alas, my end draws near. I shall die by guillotine at sunset. When my time comes, I will be taken to the *salle de la toilette*. My thick, chestnut curls will be cut off above my neck and given to Mme Richard, wife of *Le Concierge*. She makes her living creating wigs from the hair of we who have been lost to this Revolutionary fever.

My hands will be tied behind my back with care, for Sanson, our execution-er, now has much experience with this task. I will be escorted back out of the *Conciergerie* Prison through the *Cour du Mai*, where I will be heckled by a group of black-toothed women revolutionaries called *les Tricoteuse*

Charlotte in Prison

(the knitter-women), thus called because they knit clothes and bandages for the Revolutionary troops. Believed to be in the pay of Robespierre and Fouquier-Tinville, they incite the public to humiliate the prisoners of the Revolution as they make their final voyage to the guillotine.

I will be loaded with others, like cattle, into the open wooden tumbrel, and taken to the *Place de la Révolution* to face my beheading. En route down the *Rue Saint Honoré* to the guillotine, people will hurl insults, even stones, at us, further humiliating us in our final hours of life.

When we reach the *Place de la Révolution,* my fellow passengers and I will be taken, one-by-one, sometimes as many as 36 a day, up the wooden stairs to the stone platform near where the statue of King Louis XV once stood. There we will once again meet Sanson, our executioner, and his infamous blade.

Some among us will scream and beg for mercy. Others will struggle to be free. Still others will follow along, head cast downward, resigned. But I will stand erect, without remorse, for I am proud of my crime. I have murdered a murderer. I have martyred myself for the sake of the French Revolution. With my single act of violence, I will bring peace to my nation. And I will face the sharp blade of *Madame La Guillotine* looking toward the future: A future of hope for the new French Republic and all her people.

It will be up to you, and history, to judge whether my act was right or wrong.

Charlotte in Tumbrel

Charlotte Corday
on the Evening of her Death

On the evening of her death, Charlotte was forced to wear a red *chemise* (dress), the mark of her crime as a murderess. Witnesses say it poured with rain throughout the long journey to the *Place de la Révolution*. However, the weather would not scatter the crowd. The streets were so clogged with onlookers that it took two hours for the tumbrel carrying Charlotte Corday to reach its destination.

Charlotte remained standing, calm and poised, throughout the shocking ordeal. From a window overlooking the *Rue Saint Honoré*, Robespierre, Desmoulins, and Danton watched her pass.

When the tumbrel finally reached the foot of the guillotine, the rain stopped. A purple sunset flooded the sky. The terrace of the Tuileries was black with people. Charlotte mounted the scaffold steps without hesitation or assistance and gave herself willingly to Sanson's blade.

Last letter of Charlotte Corday written to her father from her incarceration in the Conciergerie Prison, 16 July 1793

Forgive me father for having disposed of my existence without your permission. I have avenged many innocent victims and prevented many more disasters. The people, when disillusioned with the Terror, will rejoice that they are rid of a tyrant.

If I attempted to convince you that I was crossing over into England, it was only because I wished to stay undercover, though I soon realized that this was impossible. I hope that you will not be tormented by this.

Farewell dear father, I beg your forgiveness. Rejoice at my exit, the cause is worthy. Kiss my sister whom I love with all my heart, as well as my parents. Do not forget Corneille's verse: "Le crime fait la honte et non pas l'echafaud."*

Tomorrow, at 8 o'clock, I meet my judge.

July the 16th, Charlotte

*The disgrace is in the crime and not the scaffold.

CHAPTER TWENTY FOUR

Epilogue

The French people of 1793 did not immediately share Charlotte's views regarding her sacrifice. They did not see her as a martyr, nor did they take Marat for a madman.

It was Marat's body, not Corday's, that received a hero's funeral. His body was placed in a proper coffin, paraded through the streets of Paris to the sound of weeping citizens, and buried at the *Panthéon*.

Charlotte's headless remains, in contrast, were tossed among those of the other victims of the Revolution into an open, pestilent, public grave.

Marat Sainted

What's more, Charlotte's murder of Marat cast a long shadow of doubt over the remaining *Girondin* delegates to the National Convention. Already in trouble for standing against the king's execution, they were believed by Robespierre and the other *Jacobins* to have been in cahoots with young Corday, even though she repeatedly insisted that they were not. Indeed, their presumed collaboration was never proven. However, all 21 *Girondin* delegates were put to death, just as Marat had wanted, on 29 October 1793.

Marie Antoinette, Queen of France, would beat the 21 *Girondins* to the guillotine by a mere two weeks.

Not quite six months after losing her husband on 21 January 1793, she also lost her son, eight-year-old Louis Charles, heir apparent to the French throne. Exiled Royalists had declared the boy King Louis XVII upon his father's death, so the revolutionaries took him from the bereaved wife and mother and placed him in solitary confinement to keep him from being rescued. He died in captivity at the age of ten.

Louis Charles

In the early hours of 2 August 1793, just two weeks after the death of young Charlotte Corday, Marie Antoinette was removed from her sister-in-law, Madame Elizabeth, and her daughter, Marie Thérèse, then aged 15. The queen bade farewell to her first born, instructing her to obey her Aunt as she would a mother.

Marie Antoinette was then spirited away through the sleeping Paris streets to the *Conciergerie* Prison, with no crowds to hamper the progress of the carriage, and no witnesses.

Marie Antoinette in the Conciergerie Prison

On 14 and 15 October 1793, the Queen of France stood before the Revolutionary Tribunal as "Prisoner no. 280," aged well beyond her almost 38 years. She was accused of treason, aiding the enemy, and inciting a civil war.

The very next day, 16 October 1793, Charles Henri Sanson arrived at work early to cut the queen's hair and bind her hands behind her back. She was loaded onto a tumbrel, made to sit with her back to the horses, and paraded through the streets of Paris before reaching the *Place de la Révolution.*

The day was fine and warm for the season. Huge crowds lined the route to *Madame La Guillotine.* Shouting "Long Live the Republic," they spat on the queen's cortège. Marie Antoinette rode to her death calm, composed, and courageous.

The Judgment of Marie Antoinette

Her head was cut clean at 12:15 and unceremoniously dumped, along with her body, into a common grave.

She had endured more than two months incarceration in the humid and airless *Conciergerie*, where she lacked all privacy – guarded both night and day – even for the most private of ministrations.

Two weeks after the fall of the *Girondins*, on 6 November 1793, cousin Philippe-Egalité also met his end at executioner Sanson's blade. As many as 20,000 people, many innocent of any real crime, lost their lives during the Reign of Terror of the French Revolution.

By 1795, the French people were tired of the bloodshed. They realized, like Charlotte, that the promise of liberty, equality, and fraternity that the Revolution once represented had long since been lost.

The most radical revolutionaries now began to turn on each other. One-by-one, they, too, found their place at the base of *Madame La Guillotine.*

- Georges Danton: Executed, 5 April 1794
- Camille Desmoulins: Executed, 5 April 1794
- Maximilien Robespierre: Executed, 28 July 1794
- Antoine Quentin Fouquier-Tinville: Executed, 7 May 1795

With no one, neither Royalist nor Republican, left to run the country, power now shifted to the French Army and, in particular, to a promising young general who had already distinguished himself in battle against the Austrian and Prussian Empires. He was a young Corsican lad, who went by the name of...

NAPOLEON BONAPARTE

About this Book

———⟫◦⟪———

Charlotte's memoir recounting the murder of Jean-Paul Marat was originally published in July 2011 as a bilingual (French-English) interactive story-based mobile app tour of Paris.

ParisAppTours: Beware Madame la Guillotine, A Revolutionary Tour of Paris, available on App Stores worldwide, went on to receive numerous commendations and awards, including:

Top 10 2011 App
School Library Journal

Top 10 2011 Tried & True Classroom App
Teachers With Apps

Top 10 2012 Educational Travel App
World Youth & Student Educational Travel Confederation

App of Distinction
Teachers With Apps

Following the success of the app, as well as feedback from teachers and librarians thousands of miles from the Palais Royal and Conciergerie, we decided to publish Charlotte's story as an interactive book for the benefit of students and educators the world over, whether or not they are planning a trip to Paris. It can now be found in iBookstores under the title, **Beware Madame la Guillotine**.

With this edition, we present the story once again, adapted for print and eBook formats and targeted to students, history buffs, and armchair travelers. We hope you enjoy it, and welcome your feedback.

Contact us at: www.timetravelertours.com, or leave us a review at Amazon.

About the Publisher

At **Time Traveler Tales & Tours**, we are revolutionizing the discovery of history and culture by bringing the very best in interactive storytelling to the mobile, tablet, and eReader formats.

Storytelling is the oldest human art form. Everyone loves a good yarn. And we believe that history is most engaging, most compelling, and most meaningful, especially for young people, when told through the stories of those who made it.

Time Traveler Tales
interactive books
bring history to life through story and games
for classroom and armchair travelers.

Time Traveler Tours
interactive mobile iTineraries
bring history to life through story and games
for youth and family travelers.

Each of our Tales and Tours take time-travelers back through the ages with a narrator whose actions helped shape their time. In telling their stories, our protagonists reveal the passions, breakthroughs, secrets, and scandals of the eras, providing an engaging and vivid understanding of their personal experiences in the context of each important historical moment.

History through Story and Games,
at the tips of your fingers.

Discover history with those who made it!

About the Author

Late at night, Sarah Towle wonders if she had been in Charlotte's shoes, would she have used the knife? She doesn't let this keep her up 'til dawn, however, as she has other stories to tell and more storyapps and interactive books to create.

Her first title, **Beware Madame la Guillotine, A Revolutionary Tour of Paris**, received accolades as a bilingual storyapp and was the inspiration for the subsequent suite of interactive books by **Time Traveler Tales**. More Paris stories by Sarah are on their way.

Sarah is represented by Erzsi Deàk of **Hen&ink Literary Studio**. She is available for author visits in person or by Skype, writers' workshops, speaking engagements, and presentations.

Special Thanks

I would like to thank all the students, teachers, families, and professionals who piloted Charlotte's original tour, helping to hone and shape the story every step of the way.

And speaking of honing, additional thanks go to my many colleagues from the **Society of Children's Book Writers and Illustrators**, most notably Erzsi Deàk, Whitney Stewart, Anne Nesbet, Tioka Tokedira, Michele Helene, and Emma Pearson Groleau, the world's greatest crit partners, all. I also send my gratitude to Stephen Roxburgh, who encouraged me to proceed with this project in the first place and who introduced me to Karen Klockner, editor of the original app version of Charlotte's story.

Thank you, all, for your editorial guidance, ongoing support, and unceasing encouragement, especially when the going got tough.

This publication would be nowhere, however, without the dedicated artist's eye of Beth Lower and the talented French-to-English translations of Charlotte's words by Liliana Hertling. Beth, I can't thank you enough for your tireless enthusiasm. And dearest Lily, your participation in this project over the years has meant the world to me. Gros bisous to you both!

Sarah Towle
Paris, France, 2014

Bibliography

Bocios, Chris. *French Architecture from Francois I - Louis-Napoleon.* Paris: Paris Art Studies Lecture Series, 2006-07.

Centre des monuments nationaux. *The Conciergerie, Palais de la Cité.* Paris: Monum, Editions du patrimoine, 2000.

Cher, Marie. *Charlotte Corday and Certain Men of the Revolutionary Torment.* New York: D. Appleton and Company, 1929.

Dickens, Charles. *A Tale of Two Cities.* New York: Signet Classics, 2007.

Doyle, William. *The French Revolution: A Very Short Introduction.* Oxford: Oxford University Press, 2001.

Fraser, Antonia. *Marie Antoinette: The Journey.* London: Phoenix Paperbacks, 2001.

Furet, Francois & Denis Richet. *La revolution française.* Paris: Librairie Artheme Fayard, 1973.

Guicciardi, Julie. *Before and After the Deluge: Aspects of the French Revolution.* Paris: WICE Lecture Series, 2006.

Horne, Allistair. *Seven Ages of Paris: Portrait of a City.* London: Pan Books, Pan Macmillan Ltd, 2002.

Jones, Colin. *The Great Nation: France from Louis XV to Napoleon.* London: Penguin Books, 2002.

Jones, Colin. *Paris: Biography of a City.* London: Penguin Books, 2004.

Le Procope: 3 siècles d'histoire. Paris: Restaurant Le Procope, 2006.

Spearman, Kelly. *The Jardins du Palais Royal: a realm of decadent elegances.* Paris: PIA Guided Tour, 2010.

Zweig, Stefan. *Marie-Antoinette.* Paris: Éditions Grasset & Fasquelle, 1933.

ONLINE SOURCES

britannica.com, for information on people and events of the French Revolution

chnm.gmu.edu/révolution, for images, political cartoons, and authentic text documents on the French Revolution

historyguide.org, for readings on modern intellectual history, in particular, the Enlightenment

marxists.org/history/france/revolution/marat, for translations of the writings and correspondence of Jean-Paul Marat during the French Revolution

wikipedia.fr, for Charlotte Corday's *Adresse aux Français amis des lois et de la paix* (Address to French Friends of Law and Peace)

wikipedia.fr, for Charlotte Corday's final letter to her father

wikipedia.org, for information on people and events of the French Revolution

Image Sources

⮞◦⮜

Cover Image & Intro Media:
Detail from: Baudry, Paul (1828-1886). *Charlotte Corday.* 1860. Oil on canvas, 203 x 154 cm. Inv. 802. Photo: Gérard Blot. Musée des Beaux-Arts, Nantes, France. Photo Credit: Réunion des Musées Nationaux / Art Resource, NY.

PART ONE: CRISIS
Detail from: David, Jacques-Louis. *Serment du jeu de paume à Versailles, 20 juin 1789 (The Tennis Court Oath at Versailles, 20 June 1789),* 1791. Photo credit: Sarah B. Towle, 2010, photographed with permission, Musée Carnavalet.

Chapter One: Meet Charlotte
Charlotte Corday. From Evert A. Duykinck. A Portrait Gallery of Eminent Men and Women of Europe and America, with Biographies. New York: Johnson, Wilson, and Company, 1873. Digital image courtesy of the James Smith Noel Collection, Louisiana State University, Shreveport, LA, http://www.james-smithnoelcollection.org.

Chapter Two: The Palais Royal
Champaigne, Philippe de (1602-1674). *Armand Jean du Plessis Richelieu, Cardinal, duc de, 1585-1642.* Photomechanical reproduction of original [LC- USZ62-100477], courtesy of the Library of Congress Prints and Photographs Division Washington, D.C. 20540 USA.

Rigaud, Hyacinthe, 1659-1743, *Louis XIV at 63.* Photomechanical reproduction of original [LC- USZC4-2032], courtesy of the Library of Congress Prints and Photographs Division Washington, D.C. 20540 USA.

Chapter Three: France in 1789
Unknown. *Le peuple sous l'ancien Régime (People under the old regime)*, 1815. Reproduction of hand-colored etching [LC-USZC4-5913], courtesy of the Library of Congress Prints and Photographs Division, French Political Cartoon Collection, Washington, D.C. 20540 USA.

Image Gallery: *Public Art at the Palais Royal.* Photo credits: Sarah B. Towle, 2010.

Chapter Four: Change Draws Near
Unknown. *Louis XVI distribue des aumônes aux pauvres (Louis XVI distributes aid to the poor)*. Crédit photographique: Musée de la Révolution Française, Vizille, France, http://www.domaine-vizille.fr, Inv. MRF 1984-20.

PART TWO: REVOLUTION
Unknown. *Fraternité.* Crédit photographique: Musée de la Révolution Française, Vizille, France, http://www.domaine-vizille.fr, Inv. MRF 1983-311.

Chapter Five: Royal Hall to Public Mall
Chevais, Jennifer. *Map of Palais Royal.* Created for Time Traveler Tours © 2010.

The Palais Royal Garden, 18th C. From Paul Lacroix Jacob (1806-1884), The XVIIIth century: its institutions, customs, and costumes: France, 1700-1789; illustrated with 21 chromolithographs and 351 wood engravings after Watteau, et al. London: Chapman and Hall, London, 1876. Digital image of color plate opposite page 346, courtesy of The Costumer's Manifesto, http://www.costumes.org.

Chapter Six: What is a Revolution?
Unknown. *Liberté.* Crédit photographique: Musée de la Révolution Française, Vizille, France, http://www.domaine-vizille.fr, Inv. MRF 1983-314.

Towle, Sarah B. *The Revolutionary Cannon*, 2010.

Chapter Seven: Peaceful Revolution
Bervic, Charles-Clément (1756-1822). *Louis XVI, King of France, 1790.* Reproduction of original engraving [LC-USZ62-82999], courtesy of the Library of Congress Prints and Photographs Division, Washington, D.C. 20540 USA.

Text Box Image: *The Tennis Court Oath.* Detail from: David, Jacques-Louis. *Serment du jeu de paume à Versailles, 20 juin 1789 (The Tennis Court Oath at Versailles, 20 June 1789),* 1791. Photo credit: Sarah B. Towle, 2010, photographed with permission, Musée Carnavalet.

Chapter Eight: A New Constitution
Unknown. *Equalité.* Crédit photographique: Musée de la Révolution Française, Vizille, France, http://www.domaine-vizille.fr, Inv. MRF 1983-312.

PART THREE: VIOLENCE
Unknown. *Prise de la Bastille (Taking of the Bastille).* Crédit photographique: Musée de la Révolution Françaises, Vizille, France, http://www.domaine-vizille.fr, Inv. MRF 1988-117.

Chapter Nine: The Mob Stirs
Unknown. *Camille Demoulins,* from a painting by Rouillard, c. 1921. Photomechanical reproduction of original [LC-USZ62-115911] courtesy of the Library of Congress Prints and Photographs Division, Washington, D.C. 20540 USA.

Text Box Image: *Other Symbols of the French Revolution. Unknown. French Constitution, Rights of Man and Citizen,* 18th c. Crédit photographique: Musée de la Révolution Française, Vizille, France, http://www.domaine-vizille.fr, Inv. MRF 1991-53.

Chapter Ten: Storm the Bastille!
Unknown. *Reveil du tiers état (Awakening of the Third Estate),* 1789. Digital reproduction of hand-colored etching [LC-USZC2-3595] courtesy of the Library of Congress Prints and Photographs Division, French Political Cartoon Collection, Washington, D.C. 20540 USA.

Unknown. *Prise de la Bastille (Taking of the Bastille).* Crédit photographique: Musée de la Révolution Française, Vizille, France, http://www.domaine-vizille.fr, Inv. MRF 1988-117.

Chapter Eleven: Louis XVI Consents
Towle, Sarah B. *Le Tricolore,* 2010.

Chapter Twelve: March of Women
Unknown. *Triumph of the Parisian Army and the People,* 18th c. Crédit photographique: Musée de la Révolution Française, Vizille, France, http://www.domaine-vizille.fr, Inv. MRF 1990-46-128.

Vigée Le Brun, Louise Élisabeth. *Marie Antoinette and her Children,* 1787. Photo credit: Sarah B. Towle, 2010.

PART FOUR: WAR
Unknown. *Sans-Culottes of the Paris Commune,* 1793-94. Photographic reproduction courtesy of the Deutsches Strumpf Museum, http://www.deutsches-strumpfmuseum.de.

Chapter Thirteen: Attempted Escape!
Unknown. *Louis XVI Stopt [sic] in his Flight at Varennes,* 18th c. Crédit photographique: Musée de la Révolution Française, Vizille, France, http://www.domaine-vizille.fr, Inv. MRF 1984-22.

Chevais, Jennifer. *Drawing of French Coin from 1792.* Created for Time Traveler Tours © 2010.

Text Box Image: *Flight to Varennes.* From, Wells, H.G., The Outline of History, 1791. New York, NY: The Macmillan Company, 1921. Downloaded from Maps ETC, on the web at http://etc.usf.edu/maps [map #03676].

Chapter Fourteen: Fractured Revolution
Philippe-Egalité. From Adolphe Thiers, Histoire de la Révolution française (10 tomes). Paris: Furne et Cie Libraires-Éditeurs, 1865 (13th edition, collection of Y.- A. Durelle-Marc). Digital image courtesy of le Centre d'Histoire du Droit de l'Universite Rennes 1.

Chapter Fifteen: Reign of Terror
Prieur & Berthault. *Siege et prise du Chateau des Tuileries, 10 Août 1792 (Siège and Taking of the Chateau des Tuileries, 10 August 1792),* 1804. Reproduction of original engraving [LC-USZC2-1498], courtesy of the Library of Congress Prints and Photographs Division, Washington, D.C. 20540 USA.

Chapter Sixteen: September Massacres

Lambert. *September Massacres (late summer 1792)*, 18th c. From Armand Fouquier, Causes célèbres de tous les peuples, t. 5, Paris, Lebrun, 1862.

George Danton. From Adolphe Thiers, Histoire de la Révolution française (10 tomes). Paris: Furne et Cie Libraires-Éditeurs, 1865 (13th edition, collection of Y.- A. Durelle-Marc). Digital image courtesy of le Centre d'Histoire du Droit de l'Universite Rennes 1.

Debucourt. *Calendrier républicain*, 1793. Aquatinte. Crédit photographique : Musée de la Révolution française, Vizille, France, http://www.domaine-vizille.fr, Inv. MRF 1987-49.

PART FIVE: MURDER

Baudry, Paul (1828-1886). Charlotte Corday. 1860. Oil on canvas, 203 x 154 cm. Inv. 802. Photo: Gérard Blot. Musée des Beaux-Arts, Nantes, France. Photo Credit: Réunion des Musées Nationaux / Art Resource, NY.

Chapter Seventeen: Death Sentence

Unknown. *An Exuberant Executioner,* 18th c. Crédit photographique: Musée de la Révolution Française, Vizille, France, http://www.domaine-vizille.fr, Inv. MRF 1984-477.

Image Gallery: *Historic Caen, Normandy.*
　　Image A: Captain Blood, *Map of the Normans' possessions in the 12th century,* courtesy of Wikimedia Commons: http://en.wikipedia.org/wiki/File:Normannen.png
　　Image B: *Allied invasion plans and German positions in Normandy.* http://www.dean.usma.edu/history/Atlases/WorldWarTwoEurope/EuropeanTheaterGIF/WWIIEurope54.gif
　　Image C: Vaugondy, Gilles Robert de (1688-1766), *Map of the généralité of Caen,* 1758. Carte du gouvernement de Normandie.

Chapter Eighteen: Marat's Murder

Jean-Paul Marat. From Adolphe Thiers, Histoire de la Révolution française (10 tomes). Paris: Furne et Cie Libraires-Éditeurs, 1865 (13th edition, collection of Y.- A. Durelle-Marc). Digital image courtesy of le Centre d'Histoire du Droit de l'Universite Rennes 1.

Robert-Fleury, Tony (1838-1911). *Charlotte Corday at Caen in 1793*. Oil on canvas, 2.100 x 1.250 m. CM177. Photo: R.G. Ojeda. Musée Bonnat, Bayonne, France. Photo Credit: Réunion des Musées Nationaux / Art Resource, NY.

Chapter Nineteen: Marat's Bath
David, Jacques Louis (1748-1825), (studio of). Detail from, *Death of Marat*, 1793. Oil on canvas, 162 x 130 cm. Inv.: RF 1945-2. Photo: G. Blot/C. Jean. Louvre, Paris, France. Photo Credit: Réunion des Musées Nationaux / Art Resource, NY.

David, Jacques Louis (1748-1825), (studio of). Detail from, *Death of Marat*, 1793. Oil on canvas, 162 x 130 cm. Inv.: RF 1945-2. Photo: G. Blot/C. Jean. Louvre, Paris, France. Photo Credit: Réunion des Musées Nationaux / Art Resource, NY.

David, Jacques Louis (1748-1825), (studio of). *Death of Marat*, 1793. Oil on canvas, 162 x 130 cm. Inv.: RF 1945-2. Photo: G. Blot/C. Jean. Louvre, Paris, France. Photo Credit: Réunion des Musées Nationaux / Art Resource, NY.

Image Gallery: *Charlotte Corday in Art History*. See images for source information.

PART SIX: PRISON
Hauer, Jean Jacques (1751-1829). *Charlotte Corday* (1768-1793), 1793, Assassin of Marat as prisoner at the *Conciergerie*. Oil on canvas, 60 x 47 cm. Inv.: MV 4615. Chateaux de Versailles et de Trianon, Versailles, France. Photo Credit: Réunion des Musées Nationaux / Art Resource, NY.

Chapter Twenty: My Capture
Charlotte Corday. Original steel engraving drawn by A. Lacauchie, engraved by Roze, 1849. Digital image courtesy of www.antique-prints.de.

Chapter Twenty-One: My Trial
Unknown. Detail from, *Trial of Marie Antoinette of Austria*, 18th c. Crédit photographique: Musée de la Révolution Française, Vizille, France, http:// www. domaine-vizille.fr, Inv. MRF 1983-323.

Text Box Image: *The Conciergerie Towers*. Photo credit Sarah B. Towle, 2010.

Chapter Twenty-Two: My Incarceration
Towle, Sarah B. *Le Greffier*, Conciergerie, 2014.

Towle, Sarah B. *La Salle de la Toilette*, Conciergerie, 2014.

Text Box Image: *Women's Courtyard*. Unknown. *The Women's Yard in the Conciergerie Prison in Paris, France*, 19th c. From G. Lenotre, Paris révolutionnaire, Paris, Firmin-Didot, 1895.

Melingue, Lucien-Etienne (1841-1889). *Le Matin du 10 thermidor an II (The morning of Thermidor 10, Year II)*, c. 1877. Crédit photographique : Musée de la Révolution française, Inv. MRF 1986-242.

PART SEVEN: BEWARE MME LA GUILLOTINE
Unknown. *An Ordinary Guillotine*, 18th c. Crédit photographique: Musée de la Révolution Françaises, Vizille, France, http://www.domaine-vizille.fr, Inv. MRF 1988-171.

Chapter Twenty-Three: The End
Hauer, Jean Jacques (1751-1829). *Charlotte Corday (1768-1793)*, 1793, Assassin of Marat as prisoner at the Conciergerie. Oil on canvas, 60 x 47 cm. Inv.: MV 4615. Chateaux de Versailles et de Trianon, Versailles, France. Photo Credit: Réunion des Musées Nationaux / Art Resource, NY.

Fournier, Mme., after Raffet. *Charlotte on the Evening of Her Death*, 1847, Lamartine's l'Histoire des Girondins (Furne and W. Coquebert), vol. 6, engraving facing page 264. Photographic reproduction courtesy Moby's Newt © 2010.

Chapter Twenty-Four: Epilogue
Unknown. *Bust of Marat*, 18th c. Crédit photographique: Musée de la Révolution Française, Vizille, France, http://www.domaine-vizille.fr, Inv. MRF 1988-112.

Unknown. *Louis-Charles, Dauphin of France*. Photo credit: Sarah B. Towle, 2010, photographed with permission, Musée Carnavalet.

Unknown. *Marie Antoinette, Queen of France (1755-1793) in Prison.* Photographic reproduction of original [LC-USZ62-116784], courtesy of the Library of Congress Prints and Photographs Division, Washington, D.C. 20540 USA.

Unknown. *Trial of Marie Antoinette of Austria,* 18th c. Crédit photographique: Musée de la Révolution Française, Vizille, France, http://www.domaine-vizille.fr, Inv. MRF 1983-323.

David, Jacques Louis (1748-1825). *Napoleon I crossing the Alps at St. Bernard.* Photomechanical print reproduction of original [LC-USZC4-7159], courtesy of the Library of Congress Prints and Photographs Division, Washington, D.C. 20540 USA.

Made in the USA
Charleston, SC
24 April 2014